The Adventure of
the Speckled Band

Sir Arthur Conan Doyle

Level 1

400 Headwords

Retold by
C.S. Woolley

The Adventure of the Speckled Band
Sir Arthur Conan Doyle

First published 2017
by Foxton Books
London, UK

This edition published 2019

Copyright © Foxton Books, 2019

ISBN: 978-1-911481-53-9

Illustrations by Alexander Solovyov

Cover design by Ed White

Retold by C.S. Woolley

Series Editor Mark Harris

Foxton Readers are a series of carefully graded books aimed at ESL / EAL learners of beginner to advanced levels. They are based on a comprehensive grammar and vocabulary framework to match each ability level and to ensure each learner progresses. They are not only suitable for ESL / EAL learners but can also be used with native speakers of primary and secondary school age.

CONTENTS

INTRODUCTION

Sherlock Holmes is the world's most famous detective. He is helped by Doctor Watson.

Helen Stoner is in trouble. Her friend told her about Sherlock Holmes. She has come to see him for help. Her sister died mysteriously after she got engaged. There is no reason for her death. The only clue is her sister's last words: *the speckled band*. She died two years ago.

Helen Stoner is now engaged. She's worried for her life. She has come to Sherlock to save her life and find out what happened to her sister. He's her only hope.

ABOUT THE AUTHOR

Sir Arthur Conan Doyle was born in Scotland in 1859. He wrote 60 mystery stories. In these stories, he wrote about Sherlock Holmes, who was a fictional detective that Doyle had created.

His notable works include *The Lost World, The Hound of Baskervilles, A Study in Scarlet,* and *The Adventures of Sherlock Holmes.*

He died of a heart attack in 1930.

CHAPTER 1

My name is Doctor John Hamish Watson. My friend is Sherlock Holmes. He's a detective. I met him eight years ago. We lived together in Baker Street. Mrs. Hudson was our housekeeper.

It was April in 1883. I woke up. Sherlock Holmes was next to me. He was dressed. It was early in the morning. It was strange. He was dressed so early.

"I'm sorry, Watson. I didn't mean to wake you," said Sherlock.

"Is the house on fire?" I asked.

"No, a lady's here to see us," said Sherlock. I got up. The lady needed our help.

I liked working with Sherlock Holmes. I got dressed and went to the living room. The lady sat by the window. She had black clothes on.

"Good morning, madam," said Sherlock.

"Good morning," she said.

"My name is Sherlock Holmes and this is Doctor Watson. Call for Mrs. Hudson, Watson," said Sherlock.

"Tea? You are **shivering**. It will help you get warmer," Sherlock said to the lady.

shiver (v) to shake slightly because you feel cold, ill or scared

"Tea? You are shivering.
It will help you get warmer," Sherlock said to the lady.

7

"I'm not shivering because I am cold," she said.

"Why are you shivering?" asked Sherlock.

"I'm **scared**," she said.

Her skin was grey and she looked very scared. She was thirty but her hair was grey. She looked much older.

"Don't be scared. I'll help you," said Sherlock. "Did you take the train this morning?" he asked.

"Do you know me?" she asked.

"No. But your ticket is in your glove. You left very early. You went to the train station in a cart," he said.

The lady was surprised.

"There is **mud** on your jacket in seven places. It's only on the left side. It's fresh. Only a cart makes mud splashes. They're the same as those on your jacket. They're on the left side because you sat next to the driver," said Holmes.

"You're right," said the lady.

"My friend, Mrs. Farintosh, told me about you. I'm scared. I need your help. I can't pay you now. I'm getting married in six months. I'll have my own money when I'm married. I can pay you then," she said.

scared (adj) afraid, frightened
mud (n) soft and wet earth

CHAPTER 2

Sherlock Holmes wrote down all his cases. He wrote in a little notebook. It was in his desk. Sherlock went to his desk and picked up the book. He looked for the notes about Mrs. Farintosh.

"Will you help me?" the lady asked.

"Yes, I will. Don't worry about the money. Now, tell us about your problem," said Sherlock.

"It is hard to explain. It's little things," she said.

"Tell me about them," said Sherlock.

Sherlock went to his desk and picked up the book.
He looked for the notes about Mrs. Farintosh.

"My name's Helen Stoner. I live with my stepfather. He's the last of the Roylott family. We live in Surrey. The family was the richest in England, but now there isn't much money left. They were lots of **gamblers** in the family before him. They lost a lot of money," she said.

"I see," said Sherlock.

"My stepfather's a doctor. He worked in India. He met my mother in India and married her. My mother was the widow of Major-General Stoner. I have a twin sister called Julia. My mother was rich. She died when we came back to England in a train crash eight years ago. Doctor Roylott took us to live at Stoke Moran," Helen said.

"What happened then?" asked Sherlock.

"We had enough money. We lived at the **estate**. My stepfather was not well. He didn't visit people. People didn't come to see him. He had arguments with everybody. He fought two men. They took him to court. He scared everyone in the village. Last week, he threw the blacksmith into a river. His only friends are the gypsies."

"Gypsies?" I asked.

gambler (n) someone who plays a game and risks losing his money on it
estate (n) a large area of land with a big house on it

"Yes, they have a camp on the estate. He visits their tents. They go walking together. He likes Indian animals too. He has a cheetah and a baboon. They walk around the estate. The villagers are afraid of coming to Stoke Moran," Helen said.

"What about your mother's money?"

"She left it all to my stepfather. When Julia and I get married, we will get our share," Helen said.

"Is the estate big?" asked Sherlock.

"Not any more," Helen said.

"Not any more?" I asked.

"The gamblers sold the land to pay their debts. It's much smaller than it was a hundred years ago. Also, it has a big mortgage," Helen said.

"How did your stepfather pay for his degree?" Sherlock asked.

"He borrowed the money from a friend," Helen said.

CHAPTER 3

"Please, go on," said Sherlock.

"Julia and I were very lonely. The servants all left. We had to do all the housework. Julia died two years ago. It was just after our birthday. She was thirty. Her hair was white," Helen said.

"Like your hair?" I asked.

"Yes. I want to talk to you about Julia's death," Helen said, "Julia went to see our aunt, Miss Honoria Westphail, two years ago. It was Christmas. She met a soldier. She got engaged to him. She came home and told my stepfather. He was happy for her. Two weeks before the wedding, Julia died," Helen said.

"Tell me all the details. Don't **leave** anything **out**." Sherlock said.

"We only use one wing of Stoke Moran. It's so big. There are many empty rooms. The bedrooms are on the ground floor. We each have our own room. They all share the same corridor. The sitting rooms are in the middle of the **manor**. The bedroom windows open outwards and the lawn is underneath them," Helen said.

leave something out (phrasal verb) to not include or talk about something
manor (n) a large house on an estate (a large piece of land)

"I understand," Sherlock said.

"Doctor Roylott went to bed early that night. He didn't sleep. He smoked his strong Indian cigars. We smelled the smoke. Julia came to my room. We sat and talked about her wedding. She went back to her room at 11 o'clock," Helen said.

"What happened then?" I asked.

"Julia stopped at the door and said, 'Did you hear the whistle last night?' I told her, 'No.' She looked at me and said, 'I heard a whistle at 3 o'clock in the morning. It was a long and low whistle,' she said. 'It's the gypsies,' I said. She went to bed and locked her door," Helen said.

"Did you always lock your bedroom doors?" Sherlock asked.

"Always," Helen said.

"Why?" Sherlock asked.

"It isn't **safe**. The cheetah and the baboon scare us," Helen said.

"I see. Please go on," Sherlock said.

safe (adj) not dangerous, free from harm or danger

"I didn't sleep that night. I was worried. It was rainy and windy. Then a woman **screamed**. It was Julia. I got out of bed and ran to her room. In the corridor, I heard the low whistle. Then a loud crash. My sister's door was unlocked," said Helen.

"Did you open the door?" I asked.

"Julia opened the door. She was white. She looked so scared. I tried to catch her. She fell to the ground. She said, 'Oh, my God! Helen! It was the band! The speckled band!' She pointed at the doctor's room. I shouted for my stepfather. He came out of his room. Julia was **unconscious**. He tried to give her brandy. Julia died in front of us," Helen said.

"So you heard the whistle and the crash?" Sherlock asked.

Helen said, "Yes."

She was white.
She looked scared.

scream (v) to make a loud cry or noise
unconscious (adj) not awake (or sleeping) because of an injury or illness

14

CHAPTER 4

"The county **coroner** asked the same question. I was sure at the time. But I'm not sure now," Helen said.

"Was your sister dressed?" Sherlock asked.

"No. She was in her nightdress. She had a burnt match in her right hand. The matchbox was in her left hand," Helen said.

"That's important. What did the coroner say?" Sherlock asked.

"He didn't find a cause of death. The windows were all **barred**. There were no holes in the walls. The door was locked from the inside. There's a chimney but it has bars inside it. She had no marks on her body."

"What about poison?" Sherlock asked.

"The doctor checked. There was no poison in her blood," said Helen.

"What do you think?" asked Sherlock.

"She probably died of fear and nervous shock," said Helen.

"Were the gypsies on the estate?" asked Sherlock.

coroner (n) someone whose job is to decide the cause of any death
bar (v) to close or fasten something (e.g. to bar a window) with a bar
barred (adj) closed or fastened with a bar (e.g. a barred window)

"Yes, they are always there," Helen said.

"What's the speckled band?" asked Sherlock.

"I don't know. She was very scared."

Sherlock shook his head.

"Please, go on," he said.

"I live alone. Percy Armitage asked me to marry him a month ago. My stepfather was happy about the news. We are getting married in the spring. The manor needs some repairs to the wall. The wall of my bedroom has a hole in it. I'm sleeping in my sister's old room. Last night, I woke up at 3 o'clock. I heard the low whistle. I got up and lit a lamp. There was nothing in my room. I got dressed and left the house. I came to see you," Helen said.

"Is that everything?" Sherlock asked.

"Yes," she said.

"Miss Roylott, you didn't tell me everything. You are protecting your stepfather," said Sherlock.

"I'm not," she said.

"You're hurt," said Sherlock.

Sherlock pushed back her sleeve. There were five marks on her wrist.

"He's a hard man. He doesn't know his own strength," Helen said. She covered up her wrist.

"Can you take us to Stoke Moran today? Can you show us your room and Julia's room? But your stepfather can't know about this," Sherlock asked.

"Yes. He's in London today. He will be in the city all day. We have a housekeeper but I can keep her away," Helen said.

"Excellent. Are you ready, Watson?" Sherlock asked.

"Of course," I said.

"We shall meet you there. Will you stay for breakfast?" Sherlock asked.

"No, I have other things to do in the city. I will see you this afternoon," Helen said.

Then she stood up and left.

Sherlock pushed back her sleeve.
There were five marks on her wrist.

CHAPTER 5

"What do you think, Watson?" Sherlock asked.

"It's a black and **evil** case," I said.

"A locked door mystery," Sherlock said.

"What do you think about the whistle and her dying words?" I asked.

"I don't know yet," said Sherlock. "There's a lot to think about; the whistles in the night, the gypsies, the speckled band, the doctor loses money when his stepdaughter gets married, and the crash."

"The crash?" I asked.

"The metal bars on the windows. Metal bars make lots of noise," Sherlock said.

"What did the gypsies do?" I asked.

"I don't know. We will find out at the manor. Who are you, sir?" Sherlock asked.

The door was open and a man stood at the door. He was a giant man. He wore a top hat and long coat. His skin was **wrinkled**.

evil (adj) bad or unpleasant
wrinkled (adj) lined or creased

"Which of you is Mr. Holmes?" he asked.

"I am. Who are you?" Sherlock asked.

"I am Doctor Grimesby Roylott of Stoke Moran," he said.

"Please sit down, doctor," Sherlock said.

"I will not! What does my stepdaughter want from you?" he asked.

"It's a little cold for the time of year," Holmes said.

"What did she say to you?" Doctor Roylott shouted.

"The **crocuses** will do well," Sherlock ignored the doctor.

"I know you, Mr. Holmes. You're a **meddler**."

He was a giant man.
He wore a top hat and long coat.

"When you leave, shut the door. There's a terrible **draught**," Sherlock said.

"I will go when I want to. Don't you dare meddle in my affairs. I'm a dangerous man. You don't want to make me angry," Doctor Roylott said.

He picked up the fire poker. He bent it with his hands. He threw it at the fire and left.

"What a nice man," Sherlock said. He picked up the poker. He straightened it out.

"Shall we have breakfast?" I asked.

"Yes. I will walk to the Doctors' Commons. I will find some information to help us," Sherlock said.

At 1 o'clock, Sherlock came home with notes on blue paper.

"I saw Mrs. Stoner-Roylott's will. When she died, her investments made £1,100 a year. Now they are £750. Julia and Helen would get £250 each when married. That left Doctor Roylott with £250 a year. Doctor Roylott has a big motive for killing Julia and Helen. We must be quick. Take your gun with you," Sherlock said.

crocus (n) a kind of spring flower
meddler (n) someone who is annoying or unpleasant; someone who likes getting involved in other people's business
draught (n) a flow of air

He picked up the poker.
He straightened it out.

22

CHAPTER 6

We went to Waterloo station and took the train to Leatherhead. Then we took a cart to Stoke Moran. It was a nice day. Sherlock sat in the cart. He had his hat on. Suddenly, he pointed at the trees.

"Look over there!" he said.

There were trees on the hill. There was an old mansion in the trees.

"Stoke Moran?" Sherlock asked.

"Yes, sir. That's Doctor Grimesby Roylott's house," said the cart driver.

"That's Doctor Grimesby Roylott's house,"
said the cart driver.

"We're going there," said Holmes.

"Take that path up the hill. It's a shortcut," the cart driver said.

We paid the cart driver. We walked up the hill. Helen walked towards us.

"Doctor Roylott's in London. He won't be back before dark," she said.

"He came to see us," said Sherlock.

"Good heavens! He followed me!" Helen said.

"It seems so," said Sherlock.

"I feel scared," Helen said.

"Don't worry. We'll help you," Sherlock said.

"Thank you," Helen said.

"Can you show us the rooms? We need to be quick," Sherlock said.

The house was an old mansion. It was in need of repair in places. It was modern on the right hand side. There was some scaffolding on the end wall. There was no hole in the wall. There were no workers.

"The lawn needs mowing," Helen said.

Sherlock stopped by the middle window.

"Is this your sister's room?" he asked.

"Yes," Helen said.

"And is this your room?" he asked.

"Yes," she said.

Holmes walked up and down the lawn. He looked at each window very carefully.

Holmes walked up and down the lawn.
He looked at each window very carefully.

"Is this Doctor Roylott's room?" he asked.

"It is. I am staying in the room next to his now," Helen said.

"Yes, because of the hole in the wall," Sherlock said.

"But there isn't a hole," I said.

"No, there's no need to repair that wall," Sherlock said.

"Is the corridor on the other side of the manor?" Sherlock asked.

"Yes," said Helen.

"Does the corridor have windows?" Sherlock asked.

"Yes, but they are very small. You can't climb through them," said Helen.

"You lock your door at night and no one can get in from the corridor. Can you please go to your room? I need you to bar your windows," Sherlock said.

We waited for her to bar the windows. I tried to open the window. "I can't open them, Sherlock," I said.

Sherlock tested the hinges.

"No one can open these windows. We need to go inside and look around," Sherlock said.

CHAPTER 7

We went in the side door. Sherlock said, "I'll look at Julia's room."

Helen showed us the room. It was a small room.

There was a low ceiling and a fireplace. It looked like a room in an old country house.

There was a brown chest of drawers in one corner. The narrow bed was in another corner.

The dressing table was next to the window. There were two **wicker** chairs in the room and a square **rug**. There was a bell rope by the bed.

wicker (n) very thin pieces of wood twisted together (see picture dictionary on page 43)
rug (n) a small carpet (see picture dictionary on page 43)

Sherlock sat in a chair.
He looked around the room.

Sherlock sat in a chair. He looked around the room.

"Who does the bell call?" he asked.

"The housekeeper," said Helen.

"It looks new," said Sherlock.

"Yes. They put it there only a few years ago," Helen said.

"Did your sister ask for it?" I asked.

"No. She didn't use it. We looked after ourselves," said Helen.

"Very strange. I need to check the floor," Sherlock said.

Sherlock got on his hands and knees. He had his magnifying glass in his hand. He checked the cracks in the floorboards. He stood up and walked over to the bed. He looked at the bed and the wall. He **tugged** the bell rope.

"It's a **fake**!" Sherlock said.

"What?" asked Helen.

"It isn't attached to a wire," said Sherlock. "It's on a hook next to the air vent opening."

"I never noticed that before," Helen said.

"There are two strange things in this room. The bell rope is fake and the air vent doesn't go outside. It goes to the doctor's room," said Sherlock.

tug (v) to pull something very hard
fake (n) an object which is not original or real

"He made a lot of changes. It took a long time. They are all very small changes," Helen said.

"Now, let's go to Doctor Grimesby Roylott's room," said Sherlock.

Doctor Roylott's room was bigger than Julia's. It had a camp bed and a small wooden shelf with books on it. There was an armchair by the bed and a wooden chair by the wall.

There was a round table and a large iron **safe**.

Sherlock walked around the room. He looked at everything carefully.

There was a round table and a large iron safe.
"What's in the safe?" Sherlock asked.

safe (n) a strong metal box with a lock used for storing money or precious things

"What's in the safe?" he asked.

"Business papers," Helen said.

"Is there a cat here?" Sherlock asked.

"No, why?" Helen asked.

"There's a saucer of milk on it," said Sherlock.

"We don't have a cat. The cheetah and baboon are the only animals here," said Helen.

"The cheetah is a cat," I said.

"A saucer of milk isn't food for a cheetah," Sherlock said.

He bent down by the chair. He looked at the seat of the chair carefully.

He stood up. He put his magnifying glass in his pocket.

"What's that?" he asked.

There was a dog lead on the corner of the bed. It was tied.

"What do you think, Watson?" Sherlock asked.

"It's a dog lead but why is it tied?" I asked.

"He's a clever man. Miss Stoner, can we go back to the lawn?" he asked.

Sherlock walked up and down the lawn.

CHAPTER 8

Is the village **inn** over there?" Sherlock asked.

"Yes, it is." Miss Stoner said.

"Can you see your windows from the inn?" Sherlock asked.

"Yes, I can," Helen said.

"Miss Stoner, listen to me carefully now, please," said Sherlock.

"Go to your room. Lock the door. Wait for your stepfather to go to bed. Then open the bars on your windows and put your lamp in the window. Your lamp is a signal," Sherlock said to Helen.

"Then?" she asked.

"Take all your things to your old room. Move quietly and lock your door," Sherlock said.

"What next?" asked Helen.

"We will do the rest," Sherlock said.

inn (n) a small hotel

"What will you do?" Miss Stoner asked.

"We will stay in your room. We will find out about the whistling," said Sherlock.

"How did my sister die, Mr. Holmes?" Miss Stoner asked.

Sherlock didn't say anything.

We took a room at the inn. We sat by the window. We saw Doctor Roylott outside. He was in a cart. He shouted at the driver.

"Watson, this is going to be dangerous," Sherlock said.

"You want me to stay here?" I asked.

"It will be safer," said Sherlock.

"You don't need me at the house?" I asked.

"I do," Sherlock said.

"Then I will come," I said.

"Thank you, Watson," Sherlock said.

"What did you see in the rooms? I saw no evil," I said.

"I saw more than you," Sherlock smiled.

"The bell rope was the only strange thing," I said.

"The air vent," Sherlock said.

"What about it?"

"They put in the air vent and the bell rope. Then Julia died. It's all very strange," Sherlock said.

"I still don't see the danger," I said.

"What about the bed?" Sherlock asked.

"There was nothing strange about the bed," I said.

"It was nailed to the floor," he said.

"How odd," I said.

"The bed had to stay next to the bell rope and the air vent."

"Oh my! Holmes, I think I understand!" I said, "What a horrible thing!"

"Yes, it is. Doctors make good criminals. They are clever and not nervous. Doctor Roylott is a bad man. Tonight will be a hard night," Sherlock said.

CHAPTER 9

We saw a light at the manor at 11 o'clock.

"That is our signal," said Sherlock.

We left the inn and walked to the house.

We walked across the lawn to the window.

The baboon jumped out of the bushes and ran across the lawn.

"My God! Did you see it?" I asked.

"We must be quick. The cheetah may attack," said Sherlock.

We took off our shoes and climbed in the window. I felt safer inside the house. Sherlock barred the window and moved the lamp to the table. He didn't make a sound. He walked over to me and **whispered**, "The smallest sound will end our plan," said Sherlock.

I **nodded**.

"We must turn out the lamp. He'll see the light through the air vent. Don't go to sleep, Watson. Your life depends on it," Sherlock said.

whisper (v) to say something very quietly because you don't want other people to hear you
nod (v) to move your head up and down to show agreement or understanding

I nodded again.

"Have your **pistol** ready. I will sit on the bed. You will sit in the chair," he said.

I took out my pistol. I sat in the chair.

Holmes had a cane. He put it on the bed next to him. He put a candle and a box of matches next to the cane. He turned off the lamp. We sat in the dark.

I'll never forget that night. It was so quiet and tense. There was no light. The shutters kept all the light out. A bird made a noise outside. I jumped. Then I heard the cheetah. The church clock chimed every fifteen minutes. It was 3 o'clock.

A flash of light came through the air vent. It disappeared again. Then came the smell of burning oil and heated metal. It was from a lantern. I sat very still.

Half-past three chimed on the clock. There was a new sound. A hiss. It was like steam from a kettle.

Holmes lit the candle and used the cane to pull the bell rope.

"Do you see it, Watson? Do you see it?" he yelled.

I didn't see it. I heard a low whistle.

We looked at the air vent. There was a horrible sound. It came from Doctor Roylott's room. The people in the village heard the sound too.

pistol (n) a small gun (see picture dictionary on page 43)

"What does it mean?" I asked.

"It's over. Take your pistol, and we'll go to Doctor Roylott's room," Sherlock said to me.

Sherlock lit the lamp. We went to the doctor's room. We knocked on the door twice. There was no answer. We walked into the room. I had my pistol. Sherlock had his cane.

"Do you see it, Watson? Do you see it?" he yelled.

CHAPTER 10

The lantern was on the table. The shutter was open. The iron safe was open.

Doctor Grimesby Roylott sat in the chair. He had Turkish slippers on his feet and wore a long grey dressing gown.

His eyes looked at the corner of the ceiling. He had a yellow band with brown speckles around his forehead.

"The band," Sherlock whispered.

I took a step forward. The band started moving.

"It's a swamp adder!" Sherlock said. "It's the deadliest snake in India. You die 10 seconds after it bites you. We need to put the adder back in the safe. Then we need to take Miss Stoner to the inn. We'll call the police and tell them about this."

Sherlock took the dog lead and put it round the snake. He threw the snake in the safe and shut the door.

We told Helen everything. She was very upset. She took a train to her aunt's house the next day. We said to the police, "It was an accident. The doctor had a dangerous pet."

"It is a swamp adder!" Sherlock said.
It is the deadliest snake in India.

The air vent and fake bell rope were the key.
The snake came down through the air vent," Sherlock said.

We went back to London.

Sherlock said, "I was wrong, Watson. I made up my mind before I knew all the facts. That is very dangerous. The gypsies were not the band. The air vent and fake bell rope were the key. The snake came down through the air vent and climbed down the fake bell rope."

"So a snake," I said.

"Yes. Its poison kills quickly and you can't test it. The coroner missed the **puncture** marks," Sherlock said.

"Then there was the whistle. The doctor trained the snake. He dropped the snake through the air vent. The milk was for the snake," added Sherlock.

"The snake was in the room with us?" I asked Sherlock.

"Yes. I heard it and lit the candle," Sherlock said.

"The steam sound!" I said.

"Yes. It attacked when I lit the candle. I used my cane to drive it off," said Sherlock.

"It went back through the air vent," I said.

"Yes and attacked its master. The cane made it angry. Doctor Roylott is dead because we are here. I'm not sorry," Sherlock said.

"No, I'm not sorry either," I said.

"Miss Stoner is safe at her aunt's house," he said.

"Yes, and she can get married," I said.

"With £750 a year," Sherlock smiled.

puncture (n) a small hole

GLOSSARY

bar (v) to close or fasten something (e.g. to bar a window) with a bar

barred (adj) closed or fastened with a bar (e.g. a barred window)

coroner (n) someone whose job is to decide the cause of any death

crocus (n) a kind of spring flower

draught (n) a flow of air

estate (n) a large area of land with a big house on it

evil (adj) bad or unpleasant

fake (n) an object which is not original or real

gambler (n) someone who plays a game and risks losing his money on it

inn (n) a small hotel

leave something out (phrasal verb) to not include or talk about something

manor (n) a large house on an estate (a large piece of land)

meddler (n) someone who is annoying or unpleasant; someone who likes getting involved in other people's business

mud (n) soft and wet earth

nod (v) to move your head up and down to show agreement or understanding

pistol (n) a small gun

puncture (n) a small hole

rug (n) a small carpet

safe (adj) not dangerous, free from harm or danger

safe (n) a strong metal box with a lock used for storing money or precious things

scared (adj) afraid, frightened

scream (v) to make a loud cry or noise

shiver (v) to shake slightly because you feel cold, ill or scared

tug (v) to pull something very hard

unconscious (adj) not awake (or sleeping) because of an injury or illness

whisper (v) to say something very quietly because you don't want other people to hear you

wicker (n) very thin pieces of wood twisted together

wrinkled (adj) lined or creased

PICTURE DICTIONARY

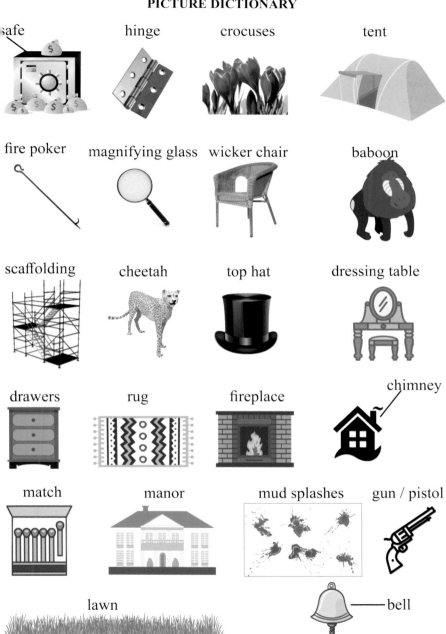

safe

hinge

crocuses

tent

fire poker

magnifying glass

wicker chair

baboon

scaffolding

cheetah

top hat

dressing table

drawers

rug

fireplace

chimney

match

manor

mud splashes

gun / pistol

lawn

bell

rope

43

COMPREHENSION CHECK

Test-1

Are the following sentences True (T) or False (F)?

1. Doctor Watson's middle name is Hamish. T / F

2. The hissing sound came from a boiling kettle. T / F

3. A lion lived at Stoke Moran. T / F

4. Her uncle killed Julia. T / F

5. Doctor Roylott smoked strong Indian cigars. T / F

6. The gypsies stayed in the house at Stoke Moran. T / F

7. Helen and Julia locked their rooms at night. T / F

8. The bell rope in Julia's bedroom was fake. T / F

9. Doctor Watson carried a pistol. T / F

10. The speckled band was Miss Stoner's wedding ring. T / F

Match the sentences.

Beginnings

1. Miss Stoner came to see Sherlock Holmes
2. Doctor Roylott met Mrs Stoner
3. The cheetah and the baboon
4. Percy Armitage asked Helen Stoner
5. Doctor Roylott went to see
6. Sherlock and Watson took the
7. Sherlock used his
8. Watson and Holmes took off their shoes
9. Watson and Holmes found
10. The speckled band was a

Endings

a. scared Julia and Helen.
b. Sherlock Holmes after Helen.
c. and climbed in the window.
d. Doctor Roylott dead in his room.
e. train to Stoke Moran.
f. when he worked in India.
g. deadly swamp adder.
h. magnifying glass to look at the floor.
i. because she needed help.
j. to marry him.

Who said this in the story?

Doctor Roylott, Helen Stoner
Sherlock Holmes or Doctor Watson

1. "Why are you shivering?"
....

2. "He borrowed the money from a friend."
....

3. "He's a hard man. He doesn't know his own strength."
....

4. "I know you, Mr. Holmes. You're a meddler."
....

5. "It's a fake!"
....

6. "Is the house on fire?"
....

7. "Don't be scared. I'll help you."
....

8. "Did you open the door?"
....

9. "What did she say to you?"
....

10. "Doctor Roylott's in London."
....

Answer the following questions.

1. What did Sherlock hit the snake with?

2. What was fake in Julia's room?

3. What street did Sherlock and Watson live on?

4. What is Doctor Watson's first name?

5. Which country did the snake come from?

6. Where did Sherlock go to find information about Doctor Roylott?

7. What is the name of Helen Stoner's house.

8. What is the name of Sherlock's housekeeper?

9. Who is Helen Stoner engaged to?

10. Where is Stoke Moran?

Test-5

Put the list in order by writing 1 to 10 in the green circles.

a. ◯ Holmes and Watson decided to go to Stoke Moran.

b. ◯ Holmes looked around the house.

c. ◯ Doctor Roylott went to see Sherlock Holmes.

d. ◯ Helen Stoner went to see Sherlock Holmes.

e. ◯ Holmes and Watson took a train to Stoke Moran.

f. ◯ Miss Stoner told Sherlock Holmes about her sister, Julia.

g. ◯ Holmes and Watson found Doctor Roylott's dead body.

h. ◯ Helen Stoner shut her door and barred her windows.

i. ◯ Helen sent a signal to Holmes from Stoke Moran.

j. ◯ Holmes found lots of strange things in Doctor Roylott's room.

Test-1

Write the positive form of the sentences as in the example.

Example: He **didn't wear** a top hat and long coat.
He **wore** a top hat and long coat.

1. She didn't take a train to her aunt's house the next day.

   ....

2. He didn't wear a long grey dressing gown.

   ....

3. The church clock didn't chime every fifteen minutes.

   ....

4. He didn't put it on the bed next to him.

   ....

5. Sherlock didn't walk up and down the lawn.

   ....

6. Sherlock didn't sit in a chair in the corner of the room.

   ....

7. We didn't wait for her to bar the windows.

   ....

8. Sherlock didn't stop by the middle window.

   ....

9. Sherlock didn't ignore the doctor.

   ....

10. He didn't pick up the fire poker.

   ....

Put these words in the correct order so that the sentences make sense.

1. was / the / lantern / the / on / table

   ....

2. rope / the / fake / is / bell

   ....

3. had / magnifying / he / his / hand / glass / in / his

   ....

4. showed / room / Helen / us / the

   ....

5. poker / the / he / threw / the / fire / at / fire

   ....

6. room / there / was / in / my / nothing

   ....

7. friend / borrowed / money / he / the / from / a

   ....

8. her / she / lives / stepfather / with

   ....

9. mud / on / jacket / there / is / her

   ....

10. the / window / the / lady / sat / by

   ....

VOCABULARY CHECK

Choose the best answer (a, b or c).

1. She .... when she saw the thief in the house.

    a. screamed   b. lost   c. smiled

2. "You are .... Put this jacket on," said his mother.

    a. warming   b. shivering   c. falling

3. He fell on the floor and lay .... for two hours.

    a. fast   b. narrow   c. unconscious

4. She keeps all of her jewellery in a ....

    a. rope   b. safe   c. cane

5. We mow the .... once a month.

    a. lawn   b. wall   c. glass

6. The professor used a .... glass to read the old text.

    a. wet   b. drink   c. magnifying

7. She bought a .... bed because her room was very small.

    a. giant   b. narrow   c. heavy

8. The builders put the .... up and then repaired the roof.

    a. scaffolding   b. nail   c. hole

9. "Don't .... in my affairs!" he told me angrily.

    a. leave   b. meddle   c. escape

10. "Put this coat on. It .... you from the wind," my friend said to me.

    a. presses   b. puts   c. protects

Match the definitions (1-10) on the right with the words (a-j) on the left.

a.	___ bar	1.	a small gun
b.	___ draught	2.	to pull something very hard
c.	___ manor	3.	to make a loud cry or noise
d.	___ puncture	4.	a flow of air
e.	___ scream	5.	a small carpet
f.	___ pistol	6.	a large house on an estate
g.	___ mud	7.	to close or fasten something
h.	___ rug	8.	a small hole
i.	___ tug	9.	soft and wet earth
j.	___ unconscious	10.	not awake, sleeping because of an injury or illness

ANSWER KEY

COMPREHENSION CHECK

Test 1	Test 2	Test 3	Test 4	Test 5
1. True	1. i	1. Sherlock Holmes	1. a cane	1. d
2. False	2. f	2. Helen Stoner	2. the bell rope	2. f
3. False	3. a	3. Helen Stoner	3. Baker Street	3. a
4. False	4. j	4. Doctor Roylott	4. John	4. c
5. True	5. b	5. Sherlock Holmes	5. India	5. e
6. False	6. e	6. Doctor Watson	6. to the Doctors'	6. b
7. True	7. h	7. Sherlock Holmes	Commons	7. h
8. True	8. c	8. Doctor Watson	7. Stoke Moran	8. j
9. True	9. d	9. Doctor Roylott	8. Mrs. Hudson	9. i
10. False	10. g	10. Helen Stoner	9. Percy Armitage	10. g
			10. Surrey	

GRAMMAR CHECK

Test 1
1. She took a train to her aunt's house the next day.
2. He wore a long grey dressing gown.
3. The church clock chimed every fifteen minutes.
4. He put it on the bed next to him.
5. Sherlock walked up and down the lawn.
6. Sherlock sat in a chair in the corner of the room.
7. We waited for her to bar the windows.
8. Sherlock stopped by the middle window.
9. Sherlock ignored the doctor.
10. He picked up the fire poker.

Test 2
1. The lantern was on the table.
2. The bell rope is fake.
3. He had his magnifying glass in his hand.
4. Helen showed us the room.
5. He threw the fire poker at the fire.
6. There was nothing in my room.
7. He borrowed the money from a friend.
8. She lives with her stepfather.
9. There is mud on her jacket.
10. The lady sat by the window.

VOCABULARY CHECK

Test 1	Test 2
1. a	a. 7
2. b	b. 4
3. c	c. 6
4. b	d. 8
5. a	e. 3
6. c	f. 1
7. b	g. 9
8. a	h. 5
9. b	i. 2
10. c	j. 10